GOOD GUY JAKE
BUEN CHICO JAKE

Written by Mark Torres

Illustrations by Yana Murashko

Translation by Madelin Arroyo Romero

HARDBALL

PRESS

Good Guy Jake/Buen Chico Jake

Copyright © 2017 by Mark Torres.

This book is a work of fiction. Names, characters, places and incidents are either the product of the author's imagination, or, if real, used fictitiously.

No part of this book may be reproduced or transmitted in any form or by an electronic or mechanical means, including photocopying, recording or by any information storage and retrieval system, without the express written permission of the publisher, except where permitted by law.

Published by Hard Ball Press.

Information available at: www.hardballpress.com

ISBN 978-0-9991358-0-8

Story by Mark Torres

Illustrations by Yana Murashko

Translated by Madelin Arroyo Romero

Cover & interior design by D. Bass

Library of congress Cataloging-in-publication data

1. Family life – fiction. 2. Labor Unions – fiction. 3. Sanitation workers –fiction. 4. Social justice.

DEDICATION

This book is inspired by and dedicated to all the past, present and future hard working brothers and sisters of the Labor movement, along with the union representatives and service professionals who have dedicated their careers to the assistance and betterment of the working class. Union strong! The book is also dedicated to my lovely wife and three beautiful children who complete me.

Jake Martin has been working for the city sanitation company for many years. He loves his work keeping the streets clean. It is a very important job.

Juan Martin ha estado trabajando para la compañía de sanidad de la ciudad por muchos años. Él ama su trabajo, manteniendo las calles limpias. Es un trabajo muy importante.

While working, Jake sometimes sees toys that have been thrown out. He takes these toys home to fix and paint, and then he gives them to the children in the local shelter. For many years Jake has enjoyed seeing the children at the shelter smile when they receive their gifts.

Durante el trabajo, Juan aveces ve juguetes que han sido tirados a la basura. Él se lleva estos juguetes a casa para arreglarlos y pintarlos, y después se los da a los niños del albergue local. Por muchos años Juan ha disfrutado ver a los niños del albergue sonreír cuando reciben sus regalos.

One snowy December day, Jake was working in Brooklyn with his partner Richie. They pulled their truck over to pick up some garbage in front of a house. Jake saw a bicycle and some boxes of toys that were thrown out so he pulled them aside.

Un día en diciembre de mucha nieve, Juan estaba trabajando en Brooklyn con su compañero Rodrigo. Estacionaron su camión para recoger basura enfrente de una casa. Juan vio una bicicleta y algunas cajas de juguetes que fueron tiradas así que las apartó.

A man in a big fancy car yelled, "Hey, I have to get to work, your truck is blocking the street!" Jake said, "I am sorry, sir. I am collecting these broken toys for children at the shelter."

6

Un hombre
en un coche grande de lujo gritó,
"Tengo que ir a trabajar, su camión
está bloqueando la calle."
Juan dijo, "Lo siento, señor, estoy
coleccionando estos juguetes rotos
para los niños del albergue."

7

As the angry man took pictures of Jake and the broken toys with his cell phone, Richie moved the truck. The man drove by very fast, nearly hitting Jake with his car.

Mientras el hombre enojado tomaba fotos de Juan y los juguetes rotos con su celular, Rodrigo movió el camión. El hombre condujo muy rápido, por poco pegándole a Juan con su carro

The next day, Jake's manager Mr. Morton told Jake he was being fired from his job. Jake was shocked and asked why.

The manager said, "Jake, you are a good worker, but a man complained that you were blocking traffic because you were taking toys from the garbage. He even took pictures of you. Jake, you know that is against the rules, right?"

Jake nodded yes and apologized, but his manager said that he had no choice but to fire him.

Al día siguiente, el gerente de Juan el Sr. Romero le dijo a Juan que lo estaban despidiendo de su trabajo. Juan estaba sorprendido y pregunto por qué.

El gerente dijo, "Juan, tú eres un buen trabajador, pero un hombre se quejó a la compañía diciendo que tú estabas bloqueando el tráfico porque te estabas llevando juguetes de la basura. Hasta te tomó fotos. ¿Juan, tú sabes que eso está contra las reglas, verdad?"

Juan indicó que sí con la cabeza y se disculpó, pero

Jake's wife Isabel did not think it was fair for the Sanitation Company to fire Jake. He was only trying to help the poor children have a happy holiday, and now *their* holiday was ruined.

Isabel no pensaba que fuera justo que la Compañía de Sanidad haya despedido a Juan. Él solo estaba tratando de ayudar a niños que viven en condiciones de pobreza tuvieran felices fiestas, y ahora *su* día festivo estaba arruinado.

Jake is a member of the United Street Cleaners Union (The USCU). They work under a contract that sets the company rules and benefits for the workers. If something bad happens to a worker while on the job, the worker can file a complaint.

Juan pertenecía al Sindicato de Limpiadores Unidos de la Calle (por sus siglas en inglés: ULUC). Ellos trabajan bajo un contrato que pone las reglas de la compañía y beneficios de los trabajadores. Si algo malo le pasa al trabajador mientras trabaja, el trabajador puede presentar una queja.

Jake asked his union representative Dalia to file a complaint against the Sanitation Company. The union complaint is called a "grievance." Dalia said she was happy to file the complaint, but she was worried the Company would reject it. "I will speak for you to the Company boss," Dalia said. "But the rule against taking toys from the trash is clear. I am afraid you don't have a very strong case here."

Juan le pidió a su representante del sindicato, Daniela, que presentara una queja contra la Compañía de Sanidad. La queja presentada por el sindicato se titula un "agravio" Daniela dijo que con gusto presentaba la queja, pero estaba preocupada de que la Compañía la rechazara. "Yo hablaré por ti con el jefe de la Compañía," Daniela dijo. "Pero la regla contra tomar juguetes de la basura esta clara. Me temo que no tienes un caso muy fuerte aquí."

Just as Dalia said, the company refused to give Jake his job back, so the union filed for arbitration. "Arbitration" is a kind of a court trial, where lawyers for both the union and the company tell their story to a judge, and the judge decides which side wins the case.

Justo como dijo Daniela, la compañía se rehusó de regresarle su trabajo a Juan, así que el sindicato presento un arbitraje. "Arbitraje" es un tipo de juicio en la corte donde los abogados del sindicato y de la compañía le dicen su historia al juez, y el juez decide cual lado gana el caso.

The trial was set for the week before Christmas. After Jake put on his best suit and tie, he and his wife walked their son to the school bus, and then they rode the subway to the arbitration.

El juicio fue citado para la semana antes de Navidad. Después de que Juan se pusiera su mejor traje y corbata, él y su esposa encaminaron a su hijo al camión de la escuela, y después tomaron el metro al arbitraje.

Jake and Isabel sat next to the union lawyer at a big table. The company lawyer, the manager and the man who saw Jake taking the toys from the trash sat across from them looking very serious. That made Jake nervous.

A woman wearing glasses said, "My name is Julia Jones. I am the judge for this case. I will hear each side tell me their story, and when you are finished, I will decide who wins the case. Do you understand? "

Juan e Isabel se sentaron al lado del abogado del sindicato en una mesa grande. El abogado de la compañía, el manager y el hombre que vio a Juan tomando los juguetes de la basura se sentaron al otro lado de ellos viéndose muy serios. Eso puso a Juan nervioso.

Una mujer con lentes dijo, "Mi nombre es Renata Hernández. Yo soy la jueza de este caso. Voy a escuchar la historia de ambas partes y cuando acaben, yo voy a decidir quién gana el caso. ¿Entienden?"

The lawyer for the company explained how Jake was removing toys from the trash, which was against the rules, plus, he was blocking traffic. The lawyer showed Judge Jones the pictures of Jake taking toys from the trash that the angry man in the car had taken. After asking the angry man some questions, the company finished its case.

El abogado de la compañía explicó como Juan estaba removiendo los juguetes de la basura, algo que estaba contra las reglas, además, el estaba obstruyendo el tráfico. El abogado le enseñó a la jueza Renata las fotos de Juan tomando los juguetes de la basura que el hombre enojado del coche había tomado. Después de hacerle unas preguntas al hombre enojado, la compañía acabó de presentar su caso.

The lawyer for the union then started his case. He explained that rules are important, but sometimes they can cause unfair results. He then asked Jake to explain what he was doing that day and why he was doing it.

El abogado del sindicato procedió a presentar su caso. Él explicó que las reglas son importantes, pero aveces pueden causar resultados injustos. Después él le pidió a Juan que explicara que estaba haciendo ese día y por qué lo estaba haciendo.

Jake told Judge Jones that he was taking the broken toys home to fix them up, paint them and give them to children in the shelter for Christmas. He wasn't taking them to make money.

Juan le dijo a la Jueza Renata que el estaba llevando los juguetes rotos a casa para arreglarlos, pintarlos y dárselos a los niños del albergue para Navidad. El no los estaba tomando para ganar dinero.

Judge Jones looked unhappy. Jake and his lawyer were afraid the judge was going to rule in favor of the company, not for the union.

La jueza no se veía feliz. Juan y su abogado temían que la jueza se fuera a pronunciar a favor de la compañía, no del sindicato.

29

At that moment, the union lawyer opened the door and waved to several children to come into the hearing room. A dozen children walked into the room. The union lawyer explained to the judge that they were from the children's shelter and they wanted to speak for Jake.

En ese momento, el abogado del sindicato abrió la puerta y señaló a varios niños que entraran al cuarto de audiencia. Una docena de niños entraron al cuarto. El abogado del sindicato le explicó a la juez que ellos eran del albergue de niños y querían hablar por Juan

The first child said, "Hello, my name is Olivia. I am here because I heard that Jake was fired from his job. Jake brought me this gift for Christmas." Olivia showed the Judge a pink scooter. "Sometimes at the shelter we are sad. When Jake gave us gifts, it made us happy. He made us feel loved."

El primer niño dijo, "Hola, mi nombre es Aranza. Yo estoy aquí porque escuche que Juan fue despedido de su trabajo. Juan me trajo este regalo de Navidad." Aranza le enseñó a la jueza un patín del diablo rosita. "Aveces en el albergue estamos tristes. Cuando Juan nos daba regalos, nos hacían felices. Él nos hacia sentirnos amados."

The second child showed the Judge a shiny green bicycle. He said, "Jake gave me this bicycle. Jake has a good heart. If he broke a rule, he shouldn't lose his job because he was trying to do something nice. Please give him a second chance.
The other children held up their toys for the Judge to see.

El segundo niño le enseñó a la jueza la bicicleta chiquita brillosa. Él dijo, "Juan me dio esta bicicleta. Juan tiene un corazón bueno. Si el rompió una regla, él no debe perder su trabajo porque él trataba de hacer algo bueno. Por favor dele una segunda oportunidad.
Los otros niños levantaron sus juguetes para que la jueza los viera.

One parent said, "Jake gave me toys for Christmas when I was a child. Now I have children of my own. I learned what the real meaning of Christmas is from him."

Un padre dijo, "Juan me dio juguetes para Navidad cuando yo era un niño. Ahora tengo niños propios. Yo aprendí el verdadero significado de la Navidad gracias a él."

37

The union lawyer showed Judge Jones a picture on his cell phone of many children and parents holding signs that said, "We love Jake" and "Give Jake his job back!" The union lawyer told Judge Jones that they were all downstairs in the lobby and wanted to come up and speak on Jake's behalf.

El abogado del sindicato le enseñó a la jueza Renata una foto en su celular de muchos niños y padres sosteniendo pancartas que decían, "Amamos a Juan" y "¡Regrésenle su trabajo a Juan!" El abogado del sindicato le dijo a la jueza Renata que todos estaban abajo en el lobby y querían subir y hablar en nombre de Juan.

Judge Jones looked over her notes from the trial and at Jake. Jake was afraid he was going to lose the trial. After a few long minutes, Judge Jones said "Jake, rules are made to be followed, not broken. The evidence is clear that you have broken the company rule, and that is not a good thing to do."

La Jueza Renata miró detenidamente sus notas del juicio y a Juan. Juan tenía miedo de perder el juicio. Después de unos largos minutos, la jueza Renata dijo, "Juan, las reglas están echas para ser seguidas, no para romperlas. La evidencia esta clara que tú has roto la regla de la compañía, y eso no es algo bueno."

The Judge went on, "There are times when a rule is broken for a good reason. When you gave the toys you fixed to the children you put a smile on their faces and warmed their hearts. You were kind, you hurt no one and you are sorry for your actions. You are a good worker and a good person. For these reasons, I am giving you your job back, so long as you promise to not break the rule again."

Jake agreed, even though he wished he could continue bringing toys to the shelter.

La jueza continuó, "Sin embargo hay muchas veces que las reglas se rompen por las razones correctas. Cuando les diste los juguetes que arreglaste a los niños, pusiste una sonrisa en sus caras y tocaste sus corazones. Tu fuiste generoso, no dañaste a nadie y lamentas mucho tus acciones. Eres un buen trabajador y una persona buena. Por estas razones, te voy a regresar tu trabajo, mientras tu prometas no romper la regla otra vez."

Juan acepto, aunque él deseaba poder continuar llevando juguetes al albergue.

The children and parents all cheered for Jake and Isabel. Outside the courthouse a Sanitation worker shouted from his truck, "We are starting a toy collection for Christmas. Every sanitation worker is bringing in toys for the shelter!"

WE A

EVERY

WE LOVE OUR
FRIEND JAKE

Los niños y padres le aplaudieron a Juan y a Isabel. Un trabajador de sanidad gritó desde su camión, "Vamos a empezar una colección de juguetes para Navidad. ¡Cada trabajador de sanidad va a traer juguetes para el albergue!"

Jake and his
wife waved back.

Juan y su esposa
saludaron
también.

46

It was a happy, happy Christmas for him and his family, and a happy holiday for the children.

Fue una Navidad muy feliz para él y su familia, y un día festivo muy feliz para los niños.

47

QUESTONS FOR TEACHERS, LIBRARIANS AND PARENTS TO ASK CHILDREN

- Sometimes people break the rules when they believe it will help fix something wrong in their community. Can you think of anyone who broke the rules and was later praised for doing so?

- Jake broke the city rules about sanitation workers taking toys from the trash. Was he right to do that, or should he have followed the rules and left the broken toys in the trash?

- Sanitation workers are called "public employees" because they work for the public — the people who live in the community. Can you name other public employees you see as you go about your day? (Hint: who is showing you this book?)

- Sometimes, public employees get hurt while they are on the job. Of all the different kinds of public employees, sanitation workers are hurt more than any other worker. Can you think how a sanitation worker might be hurt on the job?

- You have learned some new words in the story: "sanitation worker," "public employee," "union representative," "grievance," and "arbitration."

- If the Sanitation Workers in the story did not have a union, do you think Jake would have won his job back? If not, why not?

- What do you think about Jake's union? Is it a good thing for him? Is it good for the community?

- Do you think children in school should have a union? If they did, what kind of a worker would you be? What problem might you take to your "union representative" in order to make things right?

PREGUNTAS PARA MAESTROS, BIBLIOTECARIOS Y PADRES PARA PREGUNTAR A LOS NIÑOS

- Aveces la gente rompe reglas cuando creen que va ayudar a arreglar algo malo en su comunidad. ¿Puedes pensar en alguien que haya roto las reglas y después haya sido alabado por haberlo echo?

- Juan rompió las reglas de la ciudad sobre los trabajadores de sanidad tomando juguetes de la basura. ¿Él estaba en lo correcto haciendo eso, o debió haber seguido las reglas y dejado los juguetes rotos en la basura?

- Trabajadores de sanidad son llamados "empleados públicos" porque ellos trabajan para el publico - la gente que vive en la comunidad. ¿Puedes nombrar a otros empleados públicos que ves en tu día cotidiano? (Pista: ¿quien te esta enseñando este libro?)

- Aveces, empleados públicos se lastiman mientras están en el trabajo. De todos los diferentes tipos de empleados públicos, trabajadores de sanidad se lastiman mas que cualquier otro trabajador. ¿Puedes pensar en como un trabajador de sanidad puede lastimarse en el trabajo?

- Has aprendido varias palabras nuevas en la historia: "trabajador de sanidad", "empleado publico", "representante de la union", "agravio" y "arbitraje."

- Si los trabajadores de sanidad en la historia no tuvieran una union, ¿crees que le hubieran regresado su trabajo a Juan? Si no, ¿porque no?

- ¿Qué piensas sobre el sindicato de Juan? ¿Es algo bueno para él? ¿Es buena para la comunidad?

- ¿Piensas que niños en la escuela deberían de tener un sindicato? Si lo tuvieran, ¿qué tipo de trabajador serías tú? ¿Qué problema le llevarías al "representante del sindicato" para poder hacer las cosas bien?

ABOUT THE AUTHOR, ILLUSTRATOR AND TRANSLATOR

Mark Torres serves as General Counsel to Teamsters Union Local 810, a large New York City area labor union. Mark handles all of the Union's labor and employment matters, along with overseeing the Union's pension and welfare funds. Mark is also a former Engineer and union shop steward whose commitment to the Labor movement spans nearly 30 years.

Mark's debut novel, entitled "A Stirring in the North Fork", is a fictional crime thriller about an attorney who stumbles onto an unsolved murder which occurred long ago on the North Fork of Long Island.

He currently resides in Nassau County with his wife and three children.

Yana Murashko earned her bachelor's degree in 2014 at the National Academy of Managerial Staff of Culture and Arts in Ukraine, with a major in Design. Her degree qualified her as a Landscape Designer. Immigrating to the United States, she has studied English language courses at Kingsborough Community College and at the Borough of Manhattan Community College.

My name is Madelin Arroyo Romero. I was born in Mexico City and raised in Los Angeles, CA. I am adventurous and I like traveling to new places to fall in love with them and it's people. Currently, I am an ESL Instructor at a local city college and enjoy it very much.

CHILDREN'S BOOKS from HARD BALL PRESS

Joelito's Big Decision, La gran Decisión de Joelito:
Ann Berlak (Author), Daniel Camacho (Illustrator),
José Antonio Galloso (Translator)

Manny and the Mango Tree, Many y el Árbol de Mango:
Alí R. and Valerie Bustamante (Authors), Monica Lunot-Kuker (Illustrator). Mauricio Niebla (Translator)

The Cabbage That Came Back, El Repollo que Volvió
Stephen Pearl & Rafael Pearl (Authors), Rafael Pearl (Illustrator), Sara Pearl (Translator)

Hats Off For Gabbie, ¡Aplausos para Gaby!:
Marivir Montebon (Author), Yana Murashko (Illustrator), Mauricio Niebla (Translator)

Margarito's Forest/El Bosque de Don Margarito:
Andy Carter (Author), Alison Havens (Illustrator), Sergio Villatoro (Graphic Design),
Artwork contributions by the children of the Saq Ja' elementary school
K'iche tranlations by Eduardo Elas and Manuel Hernandez
Translated by Omar Mejia

Jimmy's Carwash Adventure, La Aventura de Jaime en el Autolavado:
Victor Narro (Author), Yana Murashko (Illustrator), Madelin Arroyo (Translator)

Good Guy Jake/Buen Chico Jake,
Mark Torres (author), Yana Murashko (illustrator), Madelin Arroyo (translator)

Polar Bear Pete's Ice Is Melting!
Timothy Sheard (author), Kayla Fils-Amie (illustrator), Madelin Arroyo (translator)

HOW TO ORDER BOOKS:

Order books from www.hardballpress.com, Amazon.com, or independent booksellers everywhere.

Receive a 20% discount for orders of 10 or more, a 40% discount for orders of 50 or more when ordering from www.hardballpress.com.

CPSIA information can be obtained
at www.ICGtesting.com
Printed in the USA
BVOW05*0744240917

495741BV00013B/119/P